4 (a) Draw a circle round the *lower* note of each of these pairs of notes.

(b) Draw a circle round the *higher* note of each of these pairs of notes.

5 *Above* each note write another note to make the named *harmonic* interval, as shown in the first answer. The key is C major.   [10]

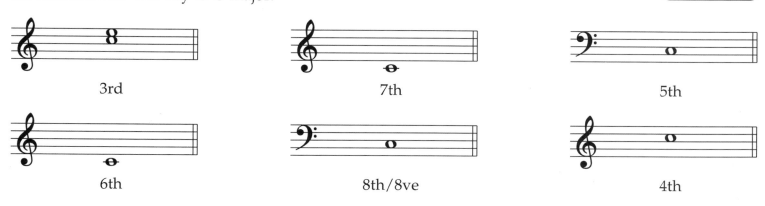

3rd   7th   5th

6th   8th/8ve   4th

6 Add a rest at the places marked ✳ in these two tunes to make each bar complete.   [10]

7 (a) Give the letter name of each of the notes marked ✳, including the sharp or flat sign where necessary. The first answer is given.   [10]

(b) This melody is in the key of F major. Draw a circle round three notes next to each other that form the tonic triad.

3

8 Look at this folksong melody and then answer the questions below.

Write your answer to question (c) on the stave below.

(a) Give the meaning of each of these: [10]

Adagio ....

pp ....

the dots below the notes (bar 2) ....

———— (bars 3–4) ....

rall. (bar 7) ....

(b) (i) The key of the melody is D major. Draw a circle round a note which is *not* in that key. [10]

(ii) Name the degree of the scale (e.g. 1st, 2nd, 3rd) of the first note of bar 4. Remember the key is D major. ....

(iii) Give the time name (e.g. minim or half-note) of the rest in the last bar.

....

(iv) In which bar is the performer told to pause or hold on to the note? Bar ....

(v) Give the letter name of the *highest* note in the melody. ....

(c) Copy out the music from the start of the melody to the end of bar 4, exactly as it is written above. Don't forget the clef, key signature, time signature, tempo marking, dynamics and all other details. Write the music on the blank stave above question (a). (Marks will be given for neatness and accuracy.) [10]

Theory Paper Grade 1   2007   B

TOTAL MARKS
100

Duration 1¹/₂ hours

Candidates should answer ALL questions.
Write your answers on this paper — no others will be accepted.
Answers must be written clearly and neatly — otherwise marks may be lost.

1 (a) Add the time signature to each of these three tunes.

10

S. C. Foster

D. Scarlatti

Berlioz

(b) Add a rest at the places marked ✻ to make each bar complete.

F.-A. D. Philidor

2 Write a two-bar rhythm as an answer to the given rhythm.

10

3 Add the correct clef and any necessary sharp or flat signs to make each of the scales named below. Do *not* use key signatures. [10]

C major

D major

4 (a) Give the letter name of each of the notes marked *, including the sharp or flat sign where necessary. The first answer is given. [10]

Haydn

G
....

(b) How many bars contain *only* quavers (eighth-notes)? ....

5 Write the time values in the correct order, from the *longest* to the *shortest*. The first answer is given. [10]

....

6 Give the number (e.g. 2nd, 3rd, 4th) of each of these melodic intervals, as shown in the first answer. The key is C major.   [10]

6th

....

....

....

....

....

....

7 Write the tonic triads named below, using the correct key signature for each.   [10]

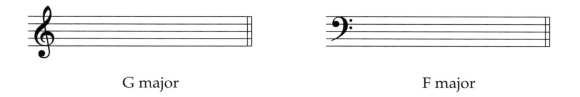

G major   F major

8 Look at this melody by J. Stamitz and then answer the questions below.

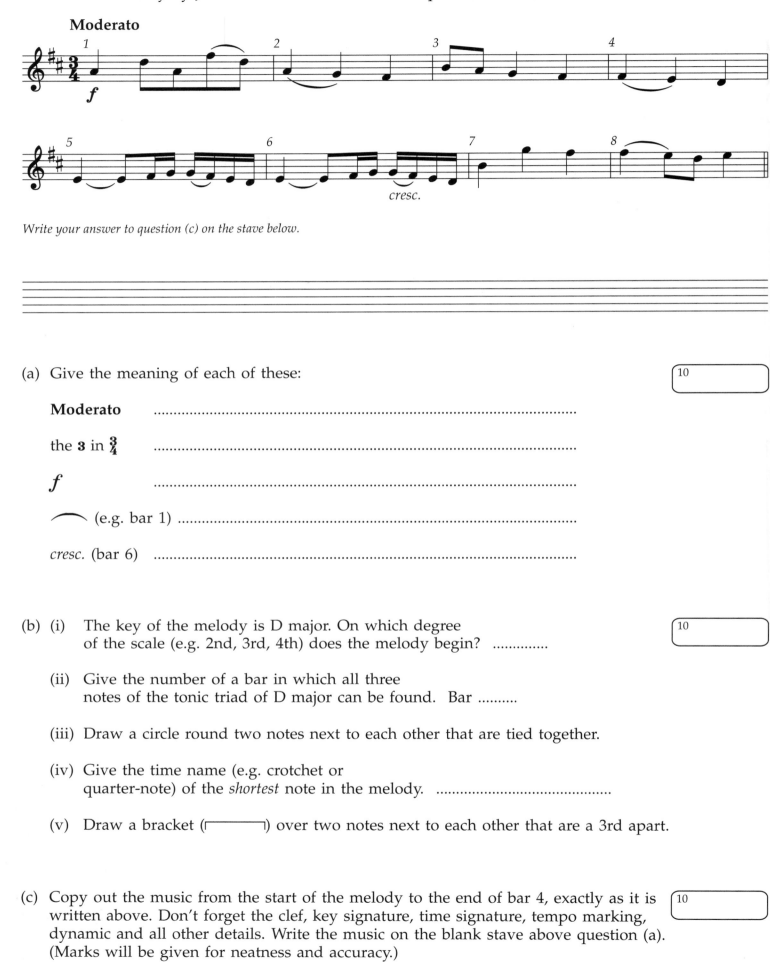

Write your answer to question (c) on the stave below.

(a) Give the meaning of each of these: [10]

Moderato   ....

the **3** in **¾**   ....

f ....

⌢ (e.g. bar 1) ....

cresc. (bar 6)   ....

(b) (i)   The key of the melody is D major. On which degree   [10]
of the scale (e.g. 2nd, 3rd, 4th) does the melody begin? ....

(ii) Give the number of a bar in which all three
notes of the tonic triad of D major can be found. Bar ....

(iii) Draw a circle round two notes next to each other that are tied together.

(iv) Give the time name (e.g. crotchet or
quarter-note) of the *shortest* note in the melody. ....

(v)   Draw a bracket (⌐‾‾‾‾¬) over two notes next to each other that are a 3rd apart.

(c) Copy out the music from the start of the melody to the end of bar 4, exactly as it is   [10]
written above. Don't forget the clef, key signature, time signature, tempo marking,
dynamic and all other details. Write the music on the blank stave above question (a).
(Marks will be given for neatness and accuracy.)

Theory Paper Grade 1   2007   C

Duration 1¹/₂ hours

Candidates should answer ALL questions.
Write your answers on this paper — no others will be accepted.
Answers must be written clearly and neatly — otherwise marks may be lost.

1 (a) Add the time signature to each of these three tunes.

10

(b) Add the correct clef to each of these tonic triads.

C major   D major

2 Write a two-bar rhythm as an answer to the given rhythm.

10

3 (a) Draw a circle round the *higher* note of each of these pairs of notes.

(b) Draw a circle round the *lower* note of each of these pairs of notes.

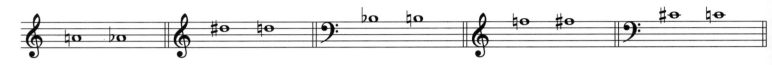

4 Name the major keys shown by these key signatures. The first answer is given.

F major

....

....

....

....

....

5 Next to each note write a rest that has the same time value, as shown in the first answer.

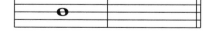

6 (a) Name the degree of the scale (e.g. 1st, 2nd, 3rd) of the notes marked **✱**, as shown in the first answer. The key is D major. | 10 |

Boyce (adapted)

3rd

....

(b) Draw a circle round two notes next to each other that are a 6th apart.

7 Name the key of each of these scales. Draw a bracket (⌐‾‾‾‾¬) over each pair of notes making a semitone, as shown in the first scale. | 10 |

Key ....

Key ....

Key ....

8 Look at this melody by F.-A. D. Philidor and then answer the questions below.

Write your answer to question (c) on the stave below.

(a) Give the meaning of each of these:

Allegretto ....

the **2** in **2/4** ....

p ....

⌣ (e.g. bar 2) ....

◁ (bar 6) ....

10

(b) (i) Give the time name (e.g. minim or half-note) of the rest in the last bar.

....

(ii) Draw a circle round two notes next to each other that are a 4th apart.

(iii) Complete this sentence: Bar 2 has the same notes and rhythm as bar ....

(iv) The key of the melody is F major. Draw a bracket (⌐‾‾‾⌐) over three notes next to each other that form the tonic triad of this key.

(v) Give the letter name of the *highest* note in the melody. ....

10

(c) Copy out the music from the start of the melody to the end of bar 4, exactly as it is written above. Don't forget the clef, key signature, time signature, tempo marking, dynamic and all other details. Write the music on the blank stave above question (a). (Marks will be given for neatness and accuracy.)

10

Theory Paper Grade 1   2007   S

TOTAL MARKS
100

Duration 1¹/₂ hours

Candidates should answer ALL questions.
Write your answers on this paper — no others will be accepted.
Answers must be written clearly and neatly — otherwise marks may be lost.

1 Add the missing bar-lines to these two tunes. The first bar-line is given in each.

10

2 Write a two-bar rhythm as an answer to the given rhythm.

10

3 (a) Give the letter name of each of the notes marked ✳, including the sharp or flat sign where necessary. The first answer is given.

10

(b) Draw a circle round three notes next to each other that form the tonic triad of D major.

13

4 Add a rest at the places marked ∗ in these two tunes to make each bar complete.

10

S. C. Foster

M. Haydn

5 *After* each note write a higher note to make the named *melodic* interval, as shown in the first answer. The key is D major.

10

5th

2nd

6th

7th

4th

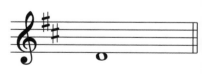

8th/8ve

6 Add the correct clef and any necessary sharp or flat signs to make each of the scales named below. Do *not* use key signatures.　10

F major

G major

7 Name the keys of each of these tonic triads, as shown in the first answer.　10

D major

....

....

....

....

....

8 Look at this melody by Puccini and then answer the questions below.

Write your answer to question (c) on the stave below.

(a) Give the meaning of each of these:

    Allegro ....

    ♩ = 152 ....

    p ....

    > (e.g. bar 1) ....

    ——— (bar 4) ....

(b) (i) Draw a circle round the *highest* note in the melody.

    (ii) Give the time name (e.g. crotchet or quarter-note) of the only rest in this melody.

        ....

    (iii) Complete this sentence: Bar 5 has the same notes and rhythm as bar ....

    (iv) Name the degree of the scale (e.g. 4th, 5th, 6th)
          of the last note of the melody. The key is C major. ....

    (v) How many bars contain a minim (half-note)? ....

(c) Copy out the music from the start of the melody to the end of bar 4, exactly as
it is written above. Don't forget the clef, time signature, tempo marking, dynamics
and all other details. Write the music on the blank stave above question (a).
(Marks will be given for neatness and accuracy.)

10

10

10

ABRSM
24 Portland Place
London W1B 1LU
United Kingdom

www.abrsm.org

Theory of Music Exams Model Answers,
2007, Grades 1 to 8 are now available
from your usual retailer.

Printed in England by Halstan & Co. Ltd,
Amersham, Bucks 02/09

ISBN 978-1-86096-872-3